When one door closes
another door opens;
we often look so long
and so regretfully
upon the closed door,
that we do not see
the ones which open for us.

Helen Keller (1880–1968)
American author, activist and lecturer

**Pictures
to share**

First published in 2016 by
Pictures to Share Community Interest Company,
a UK based social enterprise that publishes
illustrated books for older people.

www.picturestoshare.co.uk

ISBN 978-0-9934049-0-0

Front Cover:	Mrs Talmage and a Friend, 1916 (oil on canvas), Talmage, Algernon Mayow (1871-1939) / Private Collection / Photo © Christie's Images / Bridgeman Images
Front endpaper:	Woodland konradlew/istock
Rear endpapers:	Man o'War Bay antonyspencer/istock
Title page:	Daisy chain by Henry Steadman/Getty Images

Spending Time
Outside

Edited by Helen J Bate

Raindrops
keep falling
on my head...

Quotation: From song written by Hal David and Burt Bacharach
for the 1969 film 'Butch Cassidy and the Sundance Kid'

Cycling

There is always
the thin edge of danger
to keep you alert
and comfortably apprehensive.

Dogs snap at your raincoat;
potholes become personal.

And getting there is all the fun.

Rest is not idleness,

and to lie sometimes
on the grass under the trees
on a summer's day,
listening to the murmur of water,
or watching the clouds
float across the blue sky,
is by no means a waste of time.

Painting: Lunch on the Banks of the Seine 1914,
Gaston Balande (1880-1971) / Petit Palais, Geneva,
Switzerland / Bridgeman Images © unknown.

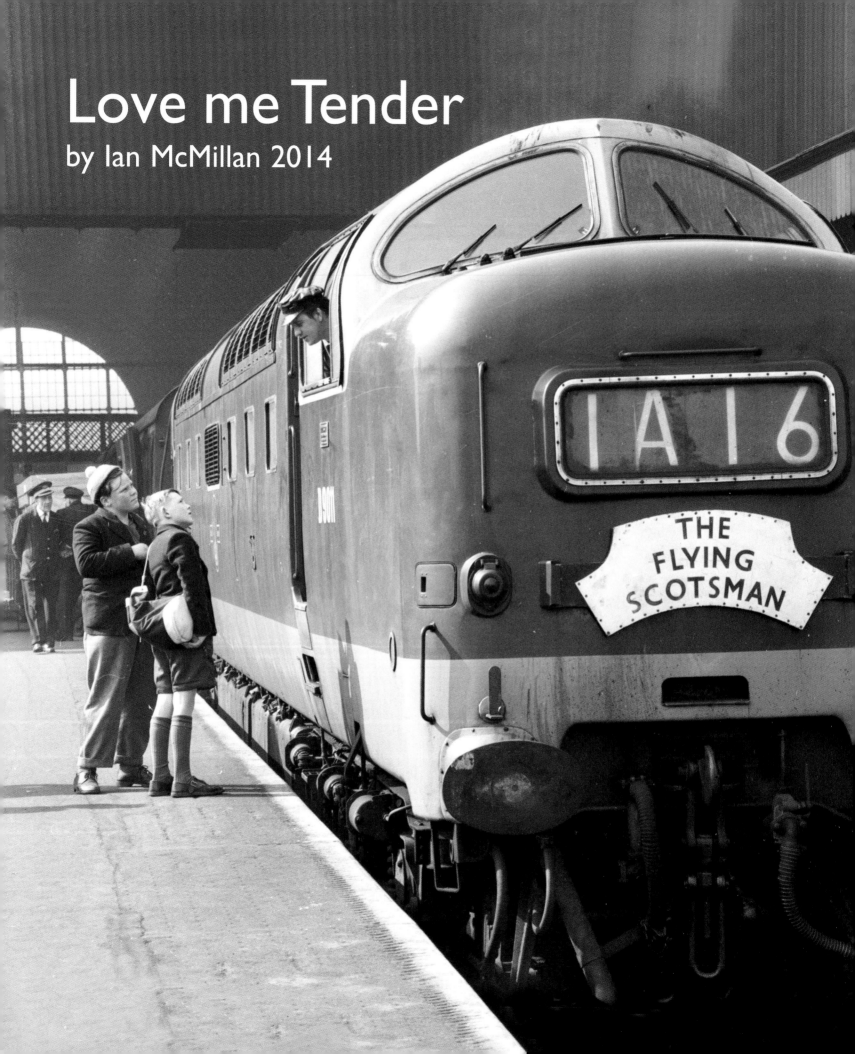

Love me Tender

by Ian McMillan 2014

It's a late-night moment on a freezing station,
A notebook with one page to fill.
It's a morning that trembles with anticipation
Of the signal, the whistle, the thrill
Of the number you thought that you'd never get
After days of frustration and weeks of regret.

It's parents and kids on an endless quest,
A Sunday weighed down by the rain;
It's the glow of a light rushing down from the West
And that beautiful, beautiful train
You now get the chance to tick off in the book
Through pure dedication and skill and good luck.

It's a map of the system laid out like a dream
A story of numbers, and tales
Of epic encounters on days wreathed with steam
When the bright sun mined gold from the rails
And you ate your sandwiches on Platform 3
And the big book of engines was light on your knee.

It's a life filled with moments that ring like a bell,
With elation, the thrill of the chase;
It's a smile from your dad that says 'Yes, all is well'
As he matches the grin on your face.
This is a hobby that never will pall.
Tomorrow's a spotting day. Well, aren't they all?

Walking the dog
in central park
New York
after heavy snow.

New York had one
of the highest
snowfalls on record
in January 2016

Our Biggest Fish

by Eugene Field (1850 -1895)

When in the halcyon days of old,
I was a little tyke,
I used to fish in pickerel ponds
for minnows and the like;
And oh, the bitter sadness
with which my soul was fraught
When I rambled home at nightfall
with the puny string I'd caught!
And, oh, the indignation
and the valor I'd display
When I claimed that all the biggest fish I'd caught
had got away!

How can you explain
that you need to know
that the trees are still there,
and the hills and the sky?

Anyone knows they are.

How can you say
it is time your pulse
responded to another rhythm,
the rhythm of the day and the season
instead of the hour and the minute?

No, you cannot explain.

So you walk.

Painting: The Walk in the Forest, (oil on canvas)
by Henri J.F. Rousseau (Le Douanier) (1844-1910)

As a child,
being out in the garden

meant playing for hours on the swing,
or helping Mum hang up a week's washing
on a washing line that stetched
the length of the garden.

Sometimes we played cowboys with cap guns,
made a tent with a wooden clothes-maid and a sheet,
or took turns to paddle in the old baby bath.

We built a snowman and watched each day
until the only patch of snow left in the garden
was where it stood.

We helped Dad plant seeds in long, straight rows;
picked potatoes, peas, broad beans,
pears, raspberries, rhubarb, plums and apples.

In the garden we kept pet tortoises, guinea pigs,
and a rabbit called Mortimer.

School children on bicycles and scooters learning
about Safety First and the Highway Code.

I love to go a-wandering
along the mountain track

And as I go I love to sing,
my knapsack on my back

valderi, valdera, valderi,
valder ha-ha-ha-ha-ha-ha

valderi, valdera,
my knapsack on my back.

A family grouped at the entrance to their tent during a weekend
holiday at the Camping Club of Great Britain and Ireland campsite
in Horsley, Surrey.

Quotation: Extract from popular song 'The Happy Wanderer'
This song recorded by the Obernkirchen Children's Choir, entered
the UK singles chart In 1954, and stayed there for 26 weeks,

The world today
doesn't make sense,

so why should I paint
pictures that do?

Pablo Picasso

Painting: At the easel 1901 by Frank W. Carter (1870 - 1933)

Daddy's taking us to the zoo tomorrow,

Text: From song, 'Going to the zoo' 'by Tom Paxton

Main photograph: Giraffe West Midlands Safari Park, UK.
Small photgraph: Baby marmoset

Putting the baby out for a nap.

In the 20th century UK parents
often left their babies outside
in their prams to get some fresh air.

Most day-care centres in Sweden
still put children outside to rest.

It's common to see rows of prams
lined up in the snow at nap-time,
with youngsters fast asleep inside.

Many still believe
that exposing babies to fresh air,
whether in the summer
or the depths of winter,
helps them to stay healthy.

Some of us
are like wheelbarrows,

only useful when pushed
and easily upset.

Messing about on the river

There are long boats and short boats
and all kinds of craft,

And cruisers and keel boats
and some with no draught.

So take off your coat and hop in a boat
Go messing about on the river.

Photograph: Lunch on the river at Henley during the Regatta.

Quotation: Song by Tony Hatch. A popular hit in 1961

Hopscotch

is a popular playground game.

Players toss a small object
into numbered squares
outlined on the ground.
They then hop or jump
through the squares
to retrieve the object.

It's said that an ancient
form of hopscotch
was played by Roman children.

The first recorded
references to the game
in the English-speaking world
date back to the late 17th century

When I was about ten years old,

we used to go out searching for birds nests
but we weren't interested in collecting the eggs.
It was just the thrill of the search,
and sometimes the tree climbing.

We wanted to find a nest with a cuckoo's egg,
but we never did.
We found nests made by all sorts of birds
including tawny owls, blackbirds, robins,
crows, hedge sparrows, woodpeckers,
jackdaws, long tailed tits, herons,
goldfinches and lapwings.

It was a great education.

A Goldfinch's nest

A Lapwing's nest

A Hunting Morning

by Sir Arthur Conan Doyle (1859-1930)

Put the saddle on the mare,
For the wet winds blow;
There's winter in the air,
And autumn all below.
For the red leaves are flying
And the red bracken dying,
And the red fox lying
Where the oziers grow.

Technology
is a queer thing.

It brings you great gifts
with one hand,

and it stabs you in the back
with the other.

Photograph: A family around their Wolseley
car during a wheel-changing operation 1954.

A Penny for the Guy

Guy Fawkes' night
is celebrated in the UK
on the 5th November.

Children often used
to build a 'Guy'
and take it around the streets
collecting money to buy fireworks.

The Guy would then be
placed on the top of a large bonfire
on the night of November 5th.

This custom celebrates
the failure of the 1605
Gunpowder Plot
in which Guy Fawkes and
twelve other conspirators
tried to blow up
the Houses of Parliament.

Extract from
'The Call of the Wild'
by Robert W Service
(1874 - 1958)

Have you gazed on naked grandeur
where there's nothing else to gaze on,
Set pieces and drop-curtain scenes galore,
Big mountains heaved to heaven,
which the blinding sunsets blazon,
Black canyons where the rapids rip and roar?
Have you swept the visioned valley
with the green stream streaking through it,
Searched the Vastness for a something you have lost?
Have you strung your soul to silence?
Then for God's sake go and do it;
Hear the challenge, learn the lesson, pay the cost.

Let us probe the silent places,
let us seek what luck betide us;
Let us journey to a lonely land I know.
There's a whisper on the night-wind,
there's a star agleam to guide us,
And the Wild is calling, calling . . . let us go.

Acknowledgements

Our thanks to those contributors who have allowed their text or imagery to be used for a reduced or no fee.

Pictures to share

Published by
Pictures to Share Community Interest Company.
Tattenhall, Cheshire

www.picturestoshare.co.uk

Printed in Europe through Beamrich Printing, Cheshire UK

Graphic design by Duncan Watts

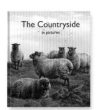
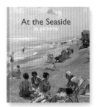

To see our other titles go to
www.picturestoshare.co.uk

Credits

Image credits not given elsewhere

Page 3 Photograph: Boy in rain Sally Anscombe/Taxi/Getty Images

Page 5 Photograph: A policeman examines a bike. Fox Photo's/ Getty Image

Page 6 Lunch on the Banks of the Seine 1914, Gaston Balande © unknown.

Page 8 Photograph: King's Cross Station in London. John Drysdale/Hulton Archive/Getty Images

Page 11 Photograph: New York snow by Timothy A Clary/Getty Images

Page 12 Young boy fishing with a net in a pond, c.1930s from a collection of photographs, tracing the history of photography, assembled by Kodak Limited and acquired from them in the mid-1980s (Photo by SSPL/Getty Images)'

Page 14 Painting: The Walk in the Forest, 1886-90 (oil on canvas), Rousseau, Henri J.F. (Le Douanier) (1844-1910) / Kunsthaus, Zurich, Switzerland / Bridgeman Images

Page 17 Photograph: Boy and rabbit. Frank Wartenberg/Getty Images

Page 18-19 Schoolchildren on bicycles and scooters learning about Safety First and the Highway Code in a practical way. Fred Morley/Getty Images

Page 21 Photograph: Family camping. Fred Morley/ Getty Images

Page 23 At the easel (1901) by Frank W. Carter 1870 - 1933 Fine Art Photographic/Hulton Archive/Getty Images

Page 24 Baby marmoset Korea. Floridapfe from S.Korea Kim in cherl/Getty Images

Page 25 Photograph. West Midlands Safari Park, Bewdley, Hereford & Worcester, UK. Marcelo Santos/Stone/Getty Image.

Page 27 Photograph:A young single mother with her baby in a pram at one of the homes run by the London Diocesan Council for Moral Welfare Work. Picture Post - I Fight To Keep My Baby - pub. 1954 Joseph McKeown/Getty Images

Page 29 Photograph: Man with boys in wheelbarrow. Mik Kemp/ Getty Images

Page 31 Photograph: Lunch on the river at Henley during the Regatta. Douglas Miller/Getty Images

Page 33 Photograph: Man playing hopscotch by Carl Smith/Getty Images

Page 35 Photographs: European Goldfinch nest and eggs. benjamint444/ istock & Northern Lapwing nest. MikeLane45/istock

Page 36-37 Young West Ham supporters at a match in the East End of London, 1960s. Steve Lewis/Getty Images

Page 39 Hunting scene. Watercolour drawing by Charles de Condamy. Frontcover of French newspaper Le-Soleil-du-Dimanche. March 18, 1900. Leemage/Getty Images

Page 41 Photograph: 1954: A family around their Wolseley car during a wheel-changing operation. Which Came First - The Woman Or The Car? - pub. 1954 / Charles Hewitt/Picture Post/Getty Images)

Page 43 Photograph: Staff and children of the Aldersbrook Children's Home, Wanstead, celebrating Guy Fawkes Day. Ron Burton/Getty Images

Page 44-45 Photograph: Mountains, Philip and Karen Smith/ Getty images

Page 46-47 Currier Ives Lithograph 1853. Charles Phelps Cushing/ClassicStock/Getty Images

Text credits not given elsewhere

Page 4 Quotation: Bill Emerson

Page 6 Quotation: The Rt Hon John Lubbock, 1834 - 1913 "Recreation," The Use of Life, 1894

Page 9 Poem Love me Tender courtesy of Ian McMillan © Ian McMillan @IMcMillan

Page 15 Text: Source unknown

Page 16 Reminiscences of H.Bate 2016

Page 28 Quotation attributed to Jack Herbert

Page 34 Quotation: K. Bate. 2016.

Page 40 Quotation: C.P. Snow, New York Times, 15 March 1971

Page 45 Extract from Poem 'Call of the Wild' by Robert W Service. Courtesy of Mrs Anne Longepe

All effort has been made to contact copyright holders. If you own the copyright for work that is represented, but have not been contacted, please get in touch via our website.